# About this Book

Each chapter of this book is based on real-life events. If you know someone with Alzheimer's disease or dementia, you are not alone.

The number of people living with Alzheimer's disease, which is just one of over 100 different types of dementia, is expected to increase fourfold by the year 2040.

There is currently no cure for Alzheimer's disease, but knowing the facts can help you improve the quality of life of those who are living with it. Educate yourself about this disease so you can help make a positive impact.

# Joining
# Grandma's
# Journey

# Joining Grandma's Journey

## Joshua Freitas

REGAL HOUSE PUBLICATIONS
-----LEARN SOMETHING NEW-----

Ordering Information: Special discounts are available on quantity purchases by corporations, associations, and others. For details, contact the National Institute for Dementia Education at:

info@nide.education

This product is endorsed by the National Institute for Dementia Education (NIDE).

National Institute for
Dementia Education

*Supportive Writing and Developmental Editing*: Angela Simonelli

*Impact Reading Group (IRG):* Melissa Jean, Ph.D., Jenel Liston M.Ed., Stephanie Silva, and Miranda Christian

Cover Illustration: Krimski Design & Communications

Interior Illustration: Regal House Publications and Krimski Design & Communications

Dear Readers,

My name is Joseph Roadsteen, and this is a story about how my family stuck together during a difficult time. When someone you love is diagnosed with Alzheimer's disease, like my Grandma was, life can become difficult. I should rephrase that – life *definitely* becomes... *different*. But, when someone you love is sick, you do whatever you can to help.

Alzheimer's disease is a brain disorder that gradually gets worse over time. It is the most common form of something called dementia, which refers to a group of brain disorders that make some parts of life difficult for people. Dementia affects the memory as well as physical and verbal skills.

When you talk to someone with dementia, you might need to repeat yourself often. They often get confused and forget a lot of things; but you will be amazed at the things you will learn from them, and the things they can still remember. My Grandma has Alzheimer's disease, but she still remembers my first birthday, even though sometimes she forgets what we did yesterday.

My advice to those who love someone who has Alzheimer's disease or dementia is to take each day as it comes. Treat the person as the person you love — not as the disease that makes life... *different*.

In the beginning, I did not know what to expect. On this journey, there were ups and downs and all arounds. Eventually, my family learned how to make things a little bit easier. We learned to adjust to our new reality, and you can too.

To help you learn more from our experiences, look for the *Comment Boxes* and *Journey Takeaways* throughout the story. They will help you summarize what you've learned so that you can apply the information to your own life.

| Comment Box | JOURNEY TAKEAWAYS: |
| --- | --- |

Very truly yours,

*Joseph*

# CHAPTER
## 1

# Why are the Keys in the Freezer?

*T*oday, Mom and I are going to the country house to check on Grandma Mae. Mom *hasn't* taken me or my sisters to visit Grandma in a while, and I know she feels guilty. The three of us kids keep her and Dad pretty busy. I have my soccer games, and my big sister, Emily, is determined to be a famous actress someday, so she has tons of rehearsals for the school play. My little sister, Bentley, has her dance classes. Plus, just being around her keeps you occupied. She asks way too many questions for an eight-year-old.

Even with everything that's going on, Mom still goes to visit Grandma, and she never complains. I mean NEVER. I honestly don't know how she does it. If I had to raise my two sisters, I would complain all the time! They are usually annoying and often unbearable.

Grandma Mae has been by herself in her house for a few days because my Grandpa Ben had surgery on his hip. He's still recovering in the hospital. Hopefully, his hip won't hurt anymore when he gets home because, unlike Mom, Grandpa Ben loves to complain. Whenever we visit, he tells me how much his hip hurts and asks me to bring him things...

"Joseph, get me that can of nuts from the cupboard," he'll say. "I'd get it myself but my hip hurts. Oh, and, Joseph, get me the newspaper from the kitchen table while you're in there." The man never says "please." To be honest, he drives me a little bit crazy, but Mom says I have to do what he asks because he's my grandpa. I love him, but I'm kind of glad he won't be home when we get there. Neither of my sisters are with us today either. So, come to think of it, today's kind of like a vacation!

Realizing this, I get a little more comfortable in the passenger seat of Mom's car and rest my head against the window. I stare out at the farms and houses we drive by, and I think about freshly baked cookies. They're always in the oven when we visit Grandma. She loves to make chocolate chip cookies with tons of chocolate -- my favorite. Usually, I eat two or three before Grandpa Ben says if I "keep eating those cookies, I'll turn into one," but then I just wrap a few more in a napkin and stick them in my pocket for later. (They end up melted and crushed in there, but I like chocolate, melted or not.) I smile, realizing that since Grandpa Ben won't be there, I can eat as many cookies as I want.

Mom slows down as we approach the little red brick house surrounded by tall evergreen trees. She turns into the driveway and parks behind Grandma and Grandpa's old car, which is covered in dust. They don't drive it anymore. Mom mentioned that maybe I could have it one day when I get my license, but I'm hoping for a car that was made sometime in this century.

"Hello?" Mom calls out politely as we walk in, as if we are strangers. This is different. We usually just walk right in, put our stuff down, and I head to the kitchen for a cookie. This *hello* thing is new. Today, when we walk in, I also immediately notice the lack of cookie-smell, and there's no hello back. We turn the corner from the foyer into the living room and there's Grandma Mae, sitting in her faded blue armchair, staring out the window. She doesn't seem to notice our arrival. It's like she's frozen in time.

After a few seconds, she turns and looks at us. Her hair is a mess, and I notice she's wearing my grandfather's glasses. His are much bigger than hers and they have black rims. Her normal glasses are small and pink. At first, I think it's weird that Mom doesn't say anything about Grandma's appearance. Instead, she just leaves the room and comes back with the right pair of glasses.

> The first signs of dementia are often subtle. They can range from not taking care of one's self to saying unusual things. It's also common for someone with dementia to accidentally take something that does not belong to them.

"Hi, Mom," my mother says, smiling as she gently places her hand on Grandma Mae's shoulder. "You've got Dad's glasses on. Here are yours."

"What?" Grandma Mae shouts, startled, blinking at Mom through the too-large frames.

Mom gently removes Grandpa's glasses from Grandma's face and replaces them with the right pair. Grandma Mae opens her eyes wide and exclaims, "Let there be light!" I burst out laughing and we all share a smile. Grandma Mae has always been funny. She knows how to lighten the mood. But, part of me still feels sad because I can tell that something's not quite right here. And, she must have had a hard time seeing out the window with the wrong pair of glasses on.

Staring out the window wearing a pair of glasses you can't actually see through... Mom says that's a sign of "depression" – or, at least that's what I overheard her saying to Aunt Rita on the phone last week. I don't know why Grandma would be depressed. She's got a nice house and an amazing grandson (ha-ha). Mom reminds Grandma Mae over and over again during our visit that Grandpa Ben will be home from the hospital next week. Each time, she says it as if she's saying it for the first time. You've got to hand it to Mom; she has the patience of a saint.

Out of nowhere, Grandma Mae turns to Mom and says, "You have beautiful eyes. What's your name again?" Then, she turns to me and says, "And who is this cute little boy?" My mouth falls open. She has done this before but still, it shocks me. Sometimes when we first arrive she doesn't recognize us right away. And, as she should be able to see, I am not a "cute little boy." I am thirteen years and 9 months old, almost fourteen! She can't blame this on her bad eyesight because she's now wearing the right pair of glasses. That's when I realize it: Grandma is losing her mind.

It is very common for someone with dementia to forget your name or confuse you for another family member or friend.

Mom inhales sharply and holds her breath for a second. "Mom, I'm Jeanette, your daughter, and this is your grandson, Joseph," she says, slowly and clearly. Then she turns to me and shrugs. She tries to smile, but the expression on her face looks as if she has just seen a ghost. I can tell a little wave of fear just went through her. She's trying to take everything in stride, but it has to hurt when your own mom doesn't recognize you.

Grandma just smiles and says, "I'm so happy you came to visit. If I knew you were coming, I would have baked cookies."

"Cookies would have been nice," I say, sarcastically. They were, after all, the primary reason that I agreed to come today.

Mom turns to me again, raises an eyebrow, and scolds, "Where are your manners?"

I try again, more politely, with a smile. "Grandma Mae, I'd love some cookies if you want to make some." Mom winks at me.

"Well, now," Grandma Mae says as she begins to rock side to side in her armchair, preparing to get to her feet. "Let's see what we can do about that."

The three of us make our way into Grandma's kitchen, and she starts to get ready to bake, washing her hands at the sink and taking her apron off of a hook in the pantry. It's strange to compare this granny-in-action, going through all the familiar pre-baking motions, to the woman staring out the window, frozen, when we first arrived. "You have to help me, okay Joseph?" Grandma Mae says, smiling at me.

You have to admit, with her messy hair and her floral apron, she's a pretty cute little grandma. "Okay," I say. I don't like baking, but at least I'll get cookies out of the deal.

"I made some cookie dough yesterday. Can you take it out of the freezer?" she asks, gesturing toward the refrigerator while steadying herself against the counter.

I open the freezer door and start rummaging through the contents, looking for cookie dough. I see a frozen lasagna and several empty ice trays, but no cookie dough. I also start to notice that, at some point, the freezer door must have been left open. Some stuff looks like it has melted and refrozen. There's a hard, sticky puddle of strawberry ice cream underneath its container.

"Whaaaaat..." I whisper in disbelief when I see them... There is a set of keys underneath a container of frozen lasagna.

People with dementia misplace things from time to time. This may become more noticeable as the disease progresses.

"Well, no cookie dough, but here are

the car keys! Can I drive the Ford around the block?" I joke, holding the keys out to Mom. She makes a face and walks over to take the frozen keys. I hand them to her and open the refrigerator door. Immediately, a bad smell fills the room. Mom and I both cover our faces with our arms, and I feel like I'm going to puke. Grandma Mae just continues to watch us, and she doesn't seem to notice the smell.

"Mom," my mom asks Grandma while shutting the fridge, "what are your keys doing in the freezer?"

We wait for her response. Is there any reasonable answer to that question? After a second, Grandma responds, "I must have gone shopping and cleaned out the freezer, and somehow my keys got in there. I don't know, Jeanette. You know I'm lost without your dad."

Oof. I pride myself on being a pretty tough guy, but that makes me sad. Mom, who pretty much always knows what to say, is suddenly quiet, too. I wait for her to say something and notice she looks scared, and for the first time in my life, I see that she doesn't seem to know what to say or do. She tosses the cold keys into the basket where they belong.

As I look through the refrigerator, pinching my nostrils closed, I see there is no cookie dough, although there is a bag of rotten broccoli that has transformed from vegetable to slimy brown mush. I guess there'll be no cookies for me! But, I don't complain because I'm not sure Mom can take a joke right now. Maybe she'll agree to stop for ice cream on the way home.

Before we leave, Mom spends a few minutes sorting Grandma's medicine out for the week, putting pills from each of the many prescription bottles into Grandma's pill organizer. Each tiny compartment is marked with the first letter of the day of the week: M for Monday, Tu for Tuesday, W for Wednesday, Th for Thursday... you get the picture. It's hard to imagine Grandma figuring it all out on her own.

"Okay, Mom, don't forget to take your medicine! And call me if you need anything! My number is on the refrigerator. We have to go pick up Emily from her rehearsal, but we'll be back soon, okay?" Mom kisses Grandma on the cheek, and so do I. Grandma smiles, and she looks alright. Maybe I'm wrong about her. Maybe she's fine.

"Okay, honey," she says sweetly as we all move toward the door. She stays in the doorway, waving to us, as we walk back down the driveway and get into our car.

Mom turns the key in the ignition, and we both buckle up: click, click, without a word between us. She puts the car in reverse, and I can hear the tires on the gravel as we roll: crunch, crunch, crunch. No music, no talking, and I am pretty sure there will be no ice cream on the way home. This awkward silence is hard for me because Mom and I always talk in the car, but right now, everything feels a little bit tense.

Mom's exuding a kind of silence I have never felt from her before. It's like she's holding her breath. Maybe it's because there's a lot to say, and she doesn't know where to begin. I know I don't. I feel uncomfortable. I want to look at Mom, but I feel afraid to. Finally, I turn my head slightly and glance at her out of the corner of my eye. She's just looking ahead, no expression on her face. Lost in thought, I guess.

And then I notice a tear slowly rolling down Mom's cheek. I watch it reach her jaw and drop off her face, landing on her shirt with an inaudible pat. My mouth opens slightly in amazement. Mom never cries. I haven't seen her cry in years... not since Bentley broke her ankle at a dance recital. Seeing her cry makes me want to cry. I want to say something to make her feel better, I just really don't know what.

Finally, I have to break the silence. "Hey, Mom," I begin, but that's all I've got so far.

It's enough to make her turn to me and smile. She wipes the tear away and grabs my chin. Finally, I feel better. So I ask her, "What do you want for your birthday this year?" She laughs. We both know I'll get her the same thing I get her every year: a homemade card, and if she's lucky, a few hours of not fighting with my sisters. I think we both know I'm only asking this question to snap her out of that sad moment. I got her to laugh, though, so I guess it did the trick.

"A million dollars," she says. Her usual answer. We both laugh. "Turn on the radio, Joe." She even lets me pick the station. "Would you like a banana split?" Mom asks, turning off the main road toward Howard's Ice Cream.

"Ummm, yes please!" Nice. Mom is back to her old self, and I hope I never see her that sad again.

12

## JOURNEY TAKEAWAYS:

✓ This visit to grandma's house shows that dementia may go unnoticed for some time and you cannot always be prepared for it.

✓ When you notice a loved one with dementia is acting differently, it can be overwhelming. Sometimes you might not know what to do or what to say. In this chapter, notice that Joseph often uses humor to cope with what he sees and feels.

✓ When Joseph notices that his Mom is struggling, he breaks the ice by bringing up a happier subject. During difficult moments, we must be gentle with each other and try to build each other up.

✓ Remember that we are all affected differently when we notice that someone we love is living with dementia. Always try your best to be kind.

*The next chapter shows how dementia can have an impact on the whole family.*

JOSHUA FREITAS

# CHAPTER
## 2

# A New Roomie

*L*ast summer, we moved from a little apartment into a new house. My parents say it's their dream home. It has a garage that we put a basketball hoop on, which is one of my favorite things about the house. We also have a backyard. At the edge of our yard is a narrow little path which leads to a pond. In the winter, the pond freezes, and you can ice skate on it. In the summer, we attach a rope to the lowest branch of the tallest tree. We swing as high as we can, then splash into the pond. I love to let go of the rope and do a backflip or cannonball... when Mom's not looking, of course.

My favorite thing about our house is that my sisters and I each have our own room. Mine is painted blue with a New England Patriots border and a queen-sized bed. My sisters are jealous I have the biggest bed out of the three of us. I remind them, Emily in particular, that she may be older but I'm almost as tall as she is, and soon I bet I'll be taller. Besides, the only reason I got the big bed is because both of my sisters got new beds when we moved. They had bunk beds in our little apartment. When my parents decided to get a new bed for themselves, I got their old one. I love how big it is. I can roll over two times and not fall off.

"Come on, kids!" Mom yells up the stairs. "We gotta go or you'll be late for school!" I'm still in my PJs, brushing my teeth. So, I pick up the pace and run down the hall to my room to finish getting ready. I hear my sisters already in the kitchen. They're always faster than me. It must be a girl thing because out of everyone in my family, my dad and I always take the longest to get ready.

We all get into the car and the seatbelts sound off: click, click, click. I'm still tired, so I put my head on the window with my backpack under it like a pillow. "Joseph," Mom says, looking up at me in the rearview mirror. "I only heard three seatbelts. Are you buckled?" I smile and buckle my seatbelt so slowly it doesn't make a sound, then say, "Yes, Mom."

We take off toward school. My sisters are talking: blah, blah, blah. I just want to sleep until we get there. Mom says, "I know it's been a long week, but I may have some news for you guys when I pick you up from school today, okay?" I open one eye, my curiosity perked. Are we finally getting a dog? A vacation? A new computer? I close my eyes again and take a deep breath, imagining all the things I want. Anything but another sister.

Mom pulls up to the drop-off spot and we all open the doors and get out as fast as possible. Even though it takes us less than a second to get out of the car, Mom stays parked there, waving at us as we all go our separate ways. The Nichols and Brown School goes from Kindergarten through 12<sup>th</sup> grade, so we all get dropped off together, but now Emily and I go to the Upper School and Bentley goes to Middle. And Mom? She just sits in the car waving until the last of us has disappeared behind the appropriate door. I know she does this because when I was little, I used to glance back from the door and wave at her one last time. But now, I wish she'd just drive. Too much waving is embarrassing.

Emily links arm-in-arm with her friends immediately on the walk up to the building. I keep my head down and walk so fast my backpack thumps against my back with every step. I swing open the door and walk in. My shoes squeak along the shiny, polished hallways as I beeline to my locker. I unzip my bag and put the stuff I don't need yet into the locker I share with Chris Mackenzie. He never keeps his side of the locker clean. I also suspect he's been stealing my pencils. The first bell rings, so I slam my locker shut and head to class.

First period: math. I take notes on how to find the square root of $x$ and forget about real life for 50 minutes. Second period: English. I'm in my seat before the next bell rings. In the pause, all I can think about is the good news my mother is going to give us after school. Maybe Aunt Rita's coming visit over February vacation? Or we're going to Disneyworld? I'm lost in my daydream when my English teacher, Mrs. Swan, walks in.

Class starts and of course she calls on me to answer the first question from last night's homework, which I suddenly realize I forgot to do. My face flushes as I confess I don't have it. I want to tell her I didn't have time because we had to drive out to see my grandma, but instead I just hope she doesn't call home. That's all I need -- to get grounded and miss out on the good news, whatever it is.

At the end of class, Mrs. Swan announces the next assignment: a 5-paragraph essay about something we're grateful for in our lives. Hmm, there are a lot of things. I love our house and the pond and my room. I'll have to think about that one.

At lunch, my mind is still stuck on what Mom is going to tell us after school. I absentmindedly eat an apple while my friend Brian sits next to me eating cafeteria pizza and talking about a new video game. I think about going to the nurse's office and pretending to be sick so Mom will pick me up early. I want to know about the surprise before my sisters.

Lunch comes and goes. Gym class comes and goes. In history class, I try to pay attention, but by the end, I am just waiting for the last bell to ring. 10 minutes left, then 5 minutes, then that sweet sound: ring, ring, ring. The school day's over. I walk to the door calmly, but the second I'm in the hallway, I run to my locker. I grab my stuff and run outside to wait for Mom.

10 minutes, 15 minutes, 20 minutes later; Mom is still not here. Emily, Bentley, and I are standing out front until the last of the other kids is gone. Emily has sent Mom three texts to find out where she is, and eventually, she just calls her. "Hey," I hear her say. "Oh, okay.... Yeah, we're fine. Uh-huh... okay. Sure, Mom. Love you, too. Bye." Emily ends the call and turns to us. "She'll be here in 5 minutes." I sit down on the curb

and look up at the sky. Just 5 minutes 'til I get the good news.

Mom's car pulls up, and right away, I see someone in the passenger seat. As she drives closer and stops, I see that it's Grandma. That's weird. We just saw her yesterday. Looks like the three of us have to squish into the back seat.

We load in one at a time. My sisters each stick their heads between the front seats and give Mom and Grandma a kiss as I buckle up. Then, as I expected, Mom says, "Joseph, are you too grown up to give your grandmother a kiss?" I unbuckle, stick my head between the seats, and give them both a kiss on the cheek.

I buckle back up and wait, expecting Mom to be as eager to tell me the news as I am to hear it. "So?" I say excitedly, "what's the news?"

"Ha!" Mom laughs. "You crack me up, Joe. Let's talk about it over dinner, okay?" Doesn't she know I've been waiting all day? I guess I can survive a few more hours.

As the streets of our neighborhood roll by, everyone in the car is pretty quiet. Emily's looking at her phone while Bentley, eyes closed, rests her head on Emily's shoulder, pretending to be asleep. Grandma gazes out the window as Mom drives.

Just then, I realize we're heading to our house, not Grandma's. Why aren't we dropping her off? Sometimes Mom picks Grandma up from appointments and gets us from school before she drives Grandma home, but Grandma doesn't usually come home with us after school, especially not on school nights. What is going on? First Mom's super late, and now we're practically on our street with Grandma still in the car.

So, I say it. "Mom, is Grandma coming over?"

"Yes," she responds, looking up into the rearview mirror. "Grandma's going to spend the night with us tonight."

Hmm, this is so weird. We do not do sleepovers with Grandma. Plus, we have nowhere for her to sleep. This makes me feel anxious. I've never been very comfortable with change. I think back to a Mindfulness workshop we did one day in Health class. When you feel stressed out, you can focus on your breath to calm yourself down. I breathe in for four seconds; hold my breath for four seconds; then I exhale really slowly. I do it over and over until I feel calmer and we arrive at home.

We pile out of the car, one by one. My sisters run straight inside, and I head straight to the garage to grab my bike. Mom goes around the car to help Grandma out and steady her on the sidewalk. Then, she walks around to the trunk. I see her grab not one but three suitcases that all look like they were made a very long time ago. They're square with little plastic handles, and they're printed all over with purple, pink, and yellow flowers. They remind me of an old shower curtain or Grandma's tablecloth.

*Why does she have so much stuff?* I think to myself. Whatever. I stand up on my right bike pedal and take another deep breath as I push the left pedal to the ground and start riding. "I'll be back!" I call out to Mom, but I'm down the street so fast I don't know whether she replied.

I ride hard and fast around the neighborhood. The wind through my hair clears my mind. People are out walking their dogs. Kids are playing in their front yards. Birds are chirping, and the sun is shining. I ride until my muscles are tired and my breathing is deep.

I bike down our driveway and straight into the garage, where I notice our camping stuff has been moved around. It looks like someone grabbed the air mattress for Grandma. *Poor Grandma,* I think to myself. She is going to have a sore back.

I walk in the front door and run up the stairs as fast as I can. That's a little game I play called, How Fast Can I Possibly Run Up the Stairs? I walk into the bathroom and turn on the shower to wash away the sweat from my bike ride. Once I'm clean, I head back to my room and open the door. What in the world? Grandma's flowery suitcases are all lined up in a row next to my bed. I don't know what's going on, but I don't like it.

"Mom!?" I call down the stairs, louder than necessary.

"No shouting, Joe. Come down here if you want to talk." Our house is too small for anyone to ever really need to yell, but I'm mad. I don't like when people go in my room without me... never mind move stuff around or put their stuff in it. My room's my sanctuary, the best place to be alone. In a lot of ways, my room's the center of my world. Mom knows this.

And she knows why I'm mad. When I stomp up to her in the kitchen, she is already prepared to speak. "Joe, you know you have the best bedroom for Grandma to sleep in tonight."

"No! Why the heck is that?" I reply, again louder than necessary. Mom doesn't say anything. I do NOT know my room is the best for Grandma. Seems to me that by definition, MY room is the best room for ME. Then, I realize the air mattress was never meant for Grandma, and my bed is bigger than Emily's or Bentley's. "Well," I stammer, preparing myself to be rude; "well, your bed's the biggest one in the house; why don't you give her your room?"

Mom gives me that look she always gives me when I say something wrong. It means I better watch what I say and do what she says. I sigh heavily, and think, *fine.* For one night, it won't be too bad. I'll put the air mattress in the living room and stay up late watching TV.

But later, over dinner, what I thought was bad gets worse. Mom tells us the real news. This arrangement is not just for tonight. Grandma is going to be staying with us, and Mom and Dad don't know for how long yet. It could be a few weeks, or maybe a month! My mind races and my heart beats faster, thinking of my room. This can't be happening.

Then Mom says it. "We'll turn the attic into your bedroom for now, Joe."

> Sometimes, families have no choice but to become caregivers for a loved one who has Alzheimer's, dementia, or another health issue. This means a loved one may move in with their family for a while to ensure their care and safety.

"WHAT?" I shout, startling everyone. "It's hot up there! And there are spiders!"

"Hey, calm down, Joe," Dad chimes in with a tone that's somewhere between scolding and soothing. "We'll get it all cleaned up." But I am not soothed. Emily and Bentley are trying not to laugh, and I shoot them a glare like the one Mom shot me earlier. I bite my bottom lip, hard.

This seems like child abuse. It's inhumane! I don't remember ever hearing worse news than losing my room. The one place where I can just relax and do my own thing. What about all my stuff? My clothes?

My autographed Gronkowski poster? The thought of Grandma sleeping in my bed beneath my Patriots poster is just weird and too unfair. My mind races through all the things that are awful about this. I feel a wave of heat flush into my cheeks and I think I might cry.

Mom sees it. She puts her hand under my chin. "If you can resist the urge to complain, maybe we'll get you a TV for the attic." She glances at Dad, and he nods.

"A big one," Dad says, and the left corner of my mouth raises up into a half smile, even though I'm trying hard not to.

"A really big one," Mom jokes, and I can't help but smile. I'm mad, but that's enticing. This is only temporary, right? I do my breathing trick: inhale deeply, exhale deeply, and eat a forkful of lasagna. Maybe I can do this.

## JOURNEY TAKEAWAYS:

✓ When someone has dementia, it does not only affect their life; it also affects the lives of everyone around them. This is why it is important to work together and communicate honestly.

✓ There will be changes. Try to keep an open mind when you are dealing with an unexpected event. One of the best things you can do is take deep breaths, calm down, and try to go with the flow.

*Next, you will learn why having patience is so important.*

# CHAPTER
## 3

# Didn't She Just Say That?

*H*ave you seen my husband? No, Grandma, I haven't seen Grandpa Ben. It's Sunday, and I'm sitting at the dining room table with Grandma, attempting to do my math homework. Tick, tick, tick; a few minutes pass, and then, there she goes again: *Have you seen my husband?*

"No, Grandma, I haven't seen him. He's still at the hospital." How many times can I repeat myself before I lose my mind?

Tick, tick, tick; every five minutes? Three!? *Have you seen my husband?* "Yeah, he's just in the bathroom," I finally say. That's obviously not true, but I just can't keep saying the same thing over and over again. I feel like I'm going insane.

> It is common for someone with dementia to repeat themselves. They may also confuse different stories or mix up facts. Try to be patient and only correct them when necessary.

How many times can she ask the same question? While I'm asking myself this question, she asks again: "Have you seen my husband?" If I keep answering her, I'll have no voice left by the end of the day. So, I try to think creatively. What if I write her a fake note from Grandpa? I flip the page of my math notebook and tear out a blank piece of paper.

"Have you seen my husband?"

"No," this time I answer, "but I think he left a note for you." I tear out the page, press it into her hands, and watch as she slowly reads it.

*Dear Mae,*

*Sorry it's taking so long, but I had to go to Springfield to buy a part for the car. I'll be back soon!*

*Love,*

*Ben*

"Hmm, she says," and seems content. I am a genius!

But a few minutes later, there she goes again. *Have you seen my husband?* "No, Grandma Mae, but he left a note for you, remember?" I give her soft hand a gentle squeeze, and once again, she reads it slowly, then seems to accept what it says.

Finally, silence! Every few minutes, I stop working to observe Grandma. Every few minutes, she looks around for Grandpa, and then she looks down at the piece of paper she's now holding with a tight grip, and the note seems to put her at ease.

> It is common for someone with dementia to ask for the people they love because those people often make them feel safe.

As the time passes, "Grandpa Ben's letter" continues to work, but I have to write her a new one frequently because she always misplaces it.

Eventually, I switch from math homework to English homework: Mrs. Swan's gratitude essay. *Well,* I think, *I've lost my room, and time at home now revolves around taking care of Grandma.* But, when I look up at her, she's smiling at me, just happy to be near me.

I write my 5-paragraph essay about Grandma and how I'm grateful to be figuring out little ways, like writing "Grandpa Ben's letter" to make life easier for all of us.

---

The days turn into weeks, and the weeks turn into months. Mom and Dad still don't know how long Grandma is staying for, but I'm beginning to understand the problem. After his hip surgery, Grandpa Ben went to a rehabilitation hospital because older people can take a while to heal after surgery. Taking care of Grandma is a lot of work, and Grandpa Ben can't do it right now. I've overheard my parents talking about how expensive it would be to have a nurse stay with her at her house all day and night. Having her stay with us seems like the only solution right now.

I'm not a monster; I love my grandma. I've stopped asking when she's leaving. Fortunately for me, her compulsive questions have slowed down, too. Grandma seems to only get stuck in "where's my husband" mode later in the evening around the time the sun is going down. Mom says this is called Sundowning – a term she read in a book, which was all about how to handle life with dementia. I guess Sundowning means that Grandma doesn't know if it is morning or night. She always gets more confused when it's dark.

> Sundowning is when a person with dementia feels more confusion around dawn or dusk. These times of day make it hard for them to know whether it is day or night, and they might experience mood changes and anxiety.

Although her questions have slowed down, Grandma does still say some crazy things. Last night after dinner, she got pretty upset and started saying, "I need to pick up the kids from the bus stop." At first, we had no idea how to respond. Then, we looked in a few books and decided to use a technique called Redirection. After we figured out that Grandma didn't have any physical needs that were making her upset, like having to go to the bathroom or being hungry or thirsty, we tried redirection.

First, we told a little white lie to calm Grandma down. We said, "Don't worry, we'll pick up the kids for you." Little fibs like these put her mind at ease. (It must be weird for Mom when Grandma talks about picking up her kids, though. Does she know Mom is her kid?)

Next, we redirected Grandma to a different activity. "Here, Grandma," I said, "you can help me with my assignment for Art class. I have to draw a Still Life. That's when you draw something exactly as you see it." We got out some paper and crayons, and Grandma calmed right now. I drew the living room sofa. Grandma drew a bunch of squiggly lines and big circles in all different colors.

Grandma has also developed some problems with her speech. I refer to this as *Word Salad,* but Mom's book says the real term is Aphasia. It's common for people with dementia to have trouble finding the right words to express themselves.

> It is very common for someone with dementia to have difficulty with speech. If this happens, try to repeat yourself slowly. Be patient and speak loudly and clearly to make sure they can hear you.

It makes me sad to see my Grandma lose her ability to communicate simple things like having to use the bathroom or that she's hungry. It's like she is going back to being a child, but not exactly — it's different.

I think of those framed black and white photos around her house: young Grandma on the day she graduated from high school, and the photo of her sitting in an old-fashioned convertible next to Grandpa Ben. I love the one of Grandma holding Mom on the train when Mom was just a baby, and the one of Grandma in her old kitchen, baking cookies, with flour all over her apron.

Grandma needs help doing some things now, and sometimes she gets confused, but she's not a child. She's my Grandma, and I will always respect her. She's seen, done, and learned lots of things in her life even if she

can't tell me about all of them anymore.
She deserves love, respect, and dignity.

# JOURNEY TAKEAWAYS:

✓ Remember someone who has dementia will repeat themselves sometimes. Try to be creative and come up with a few different responses to keep the conversation new.

✓ It can be best to allow them to believe something that is not true, rather than contradicting or correcting them. This is what we call, "joining the journey." Allow the conversation to go wherever it goes.

✓ We are all taught not to lie. But when someone has dementia, it can be okay to say something like, "we picked up your kids for you" or "we just went grocery shopping" when you really didn't. You are not lying with the intention of deceiving them; you are just saying something to put their mind at ease and make them feel safe and calm.

✓ Joseph reminded us that, even though his Grandma has lost some skills and memories, she is not a child. This is important because we must respect our elders who have dementia. They deserve the same respect that you have always given them, plus some extra love and compassion.

# CHAPTER
## 4

# Time Changes Everything

*T*hree months later, Grandma and Grandpa are both living with us. After Grandpa's hip healed, everyone talked about Grandma going back home for them to live together like usual. But, in the end, it became obvious it would be way too much work for Grandpa to take care of Grandma by himself. Mom said they would have to hire nurses to be there pretty much all the time.

So now, Grandma and Grandpa are just part of the regular atmosphere of our home. The good news is Grandpa Ben and I are getting along much better. The other day, he said to me, "Hey, Joe, I appreciate the sacrifice you made to let us stay in your room." That's the nicest thing Grandpa Ben has ever said to me! He has also really helped me turn the attic into my own man-cave by giving me his old dart board. I also got to frame my posters and put them up with nails instead of tape because Mom doesn't care if I put holes in the attic walls. When my best friend, Brian, comes over, it's like we have our own hideaway. We play video games on my new TV, which is pretty amazing, and we don't have to include my sisters.

I would never have thought that giving up my old room would have any benefits, and I'm happy to say it has! I think I actually like the attic more than my old room now... but let's keep that our little secret. If I told my family, it would ruin all my leverage.

Last month, Mom quit her job at the bank to stay home with Grandma and

Grandpa full-time. Now, she works a couple of nights a week at Josie's Diner in the town center. On those nights, the rest of us take care of the grandparents and fend for ourselves. I guess Mom still needs to make some money, or maybe she just needs a reason to get out of the house.

Before Grandma and Grandpa moved in, there were already a million places for Mom to drive to and things for her to do around the house. But, with Grandma and Grandpa both here, the jobs have multiplied by about a thousand. There are doctor's appointments, trips to the pharmacy, and two more mouths to feed.

Emily got her driver's license, so she helps out a little more – running errands or driving herself to theater rehearsals and friends' houses. Most days, Emily drives Bentley and me to school with her now, which I admit makes me feel pretty cool.

Mom and Dad ended up giving Emily Grandma and Grandpa's beat up old car, which I make fun of her about. But, an old car is better than no car at all. I can't wait to get my license in a couple of years!

Everyone's trying their best to make things work out with Grandma and

Grandpa. But lately, Mom seems to have a short fuse for little things like when nobody empties the dishwasher or if I leave my dirty clothes on top of the washing machine for too long. I forgot to put the trash barrels out the other night, and you would have thought I threw trash all over the living room by the way she reacted.

"Joseph!" she yelled up the stairs to me. So much for her no-yelling-in-the-house rule. "Why are the trashcans still on the side of the house? You need to bring them to curb! How many times do I need to tell you?"

"Sor-ryyy," I whined in mock apology as I jogged downstairs to do my chore, but she wasn't finished.

"I can't do everything around here!" she snapped. "You have to pitch in!"

"Okay!" I said, but in my head, I was thinking, *Sheesh, Mom -- chill.* I don't like when she freaks out on me but I bite my tongue because I know she's going through a lot. I try to be a good kid. To be honest, Dad doesn't do half as much as Mom does around the house, and my sisters and I should help out more than we do.

When Mom gets overwhelmed, Dad tries to help, but sometimes he just can't take it. On those days, he rolls his eyes and goes out to the garage to work on his car instead. Dad works a lot during the week, and Grandma and Grandpa are Mom's parents after all.

Of course, we're all family, and Dad loves Grandma and Grandpa... but Dad also has another love: his car. Dad's car is like his fourth child. It's a cherry-red, 1957 Chevy with two white stripes along the sides. It's so old there are no seatbelts! (Apparently, a long time ago, cars weren't very safe, but they sure were pretty.) Dad loves to take his car out for drives on Sundays, particularly when he "just needs a break."

A couple of years ago, I was in a rush one morning, and I threw my bike in the garage. It wheeled itself right into the side of Dad's car. The bike's pedal scratched a three-inch jagged line into the bottom of the passenger door. I was so nervous about how Dad would react that I told Mom right away. Even if I got in trouble with Mom, I knew it wouldn't be half as bad as telling Dad I scratched his precious car!

Mom was really cool about it. "Accidents happen," she said; "just be more careful next time." She and I went to the store and got a tube of red touchup paint to fill in the scratch. When we were finished, it looked perfect. We never told Dad, and as far as I know, he's never noticed. Thinking back, Mom's a lot different these days than she was when she helped me fix the scratch. Lately, she's a lot more stressed and a lot less easygoing.

> Joseph's mom is the primary caregiver to both Joseph's grandma and grandpa, which means she does most of the work. That can be very overwhelming. Try your best to help!

Mom doesn't see her friends as much as Dad sees his. She talks to them on the phone sometimes, but they never get together because Mom never has enough time. Sometimes, Dad's friends come over to hang out if Mom takes a Saturday night shift at Josie's Diner. They hang out in the garage listening to what he calls Classic Rock. (I call it Dad Rock.) A couple of times, I've overheard my Dad complain to his friends about how full the house is right now or how stressed out Mom's been. I hope Mom hasn't heard him say those things. I think it would make her feel even worse about everything.

Even though Dad sometimes complains to his friends, I know how much he loves our family. And he always treats Grandma and Grandpa with kindness. He would never make them feel unwelcome, even when they're being difficult. For the most part, Dad cracks jokes with Grandpa Ben and is gentle and patient around Grandma.

When my parents got married, my grandparents paid for their wedding, which Mom and Dad's friends say was the most extravagant wedding ever. I think they also helped my parents buy our new house. Dad's taught me that it would be rude to be disrespectful to people who have given you so much, but I don't think it's about money. I think it's about family.

Life in a house filled with seven people, one of whom has dementia, has certainly changed all of us. But, "this is just what families do," Mom says. "Some times are good; some times are tough. That's life."

As the days go by, I feel like my Grandma's mind is truly starting to slip away. She spends a lot of time in the living room, watching TV. Sometimes, Mom gives her little chores to do around the house, like cleaning the kitchen counters. But, Mom always has to re-clean them because Grandma takes forever on the very same spot, or she makes it across the whole counter but misses a lot of places or forgets to rinse the sponge.

Mom pretty much always tells little white lies to Grandma to get her to do things now. This morning, Grandma thought she had taken a shower, but in reality, she hadn't taken one in three days. So, Mom told her we were going to church just to get her into the shower. Of course, by the time they finished her shower, Grandma had forgotten about church, so you must admit, the technique is effective. What was once the occasional white lie has become our new normal.

Mom's friend Mary came to visit a couple of days ago. Mary's a nurse, and she told Mom there's a support group at the nearby nursing home for families of people with dementia to go to.

Apparently, a support group is like a community meeting for people who are all

JOINING GRANDMA'S JOURNEY

dealing with the same kind of issue. It sounds good to me but Mom doesn't want to go. She's been to the nursing home more than once to check the place out, but she keeps saying she's not ready to send Grandma to "one of those places." I guess she thinks they're not nice places.

But Mary said they have activities and entertainment, and apparently the kitchen is always open, which sounds awesome to me. I imagine Grandma and Grandpa making friends with people their age — playing ping-pong or listening to old-timey music together. I bet Grandpa would have fun there; but I'm not sure Mom will ever agree to move Grandma and Grandpa out of our house. Even with all the stress it's causing her to take care of them, she says it would make her feel like a failure not to take care of them herself.

## JOURNEY TAKEAWAYS:

✓ Remember, you are part of a team. When you work together, great things can happen.

✓ In this chapter, you learned it is okay to talk to a friend when you are feeling overwhelmed. Joseph's dad finds relief in venting to his friends; and even though Joseph's mom is really busy, it's good for her to talk to friends on the phone. A friend or family member who is willing to listen can really help you get through stressful times.

✓ You also learned the term "primary caregiver," which refers to the person who provides most of the care. On most teams, there is a leader; and with a caregiving team, the leader is the primary caregiver. Remember to help them out as much as you can. Doing something nice for them or helping around the house can make a big difference.

# CHAPTER
## 5

# My First Date

*T*hings at home had been taking a lot of my energy, but I couldn't help but be distracted by one particular girl in my class. Her name is Tina Brown, and just thinking about how much I like her makes me feel better. It's taken me a month to get up the guts to ask her if she'll go to the semi-formal dance with me... partially because I'm scared, but also because I know how much my sisters are going to tease me about it when they find out. Sure enough, Emily figured out that I like Tina and now both my sisters sing "Joseph's got a giiiirlfriend" and "Joseph and Tina, sittin' in a tree, k-i-s-s-i-n-g" at me at least three times a day.

Tina and I have been friends all school year, ever since the day we skipped gym class together. It was Dodgeball Day, which in my opinion is a brutal sport that only crazy people actually enjoy. Apparently, Tina agrees. Our eyes met and we shared a look of mutual dread. I love sports, but let's just say, when it comes to dodgeball, I like Tina much better.

Tina nodded her head toward the side door of the gym and I knew she was asking me if I wanted to escape from the dodgeball torture. I smiled and nodded, and the first time Mr. Skinner turned his back, we tip-toed out the door silently, each holding our breath so we wouldn't laugh. It was the first time I've ever cut class, and it felt scary and exciting at the same time.

The gym door exits to the sports field, beyond which is the baseball diamond. We ran across the field, holding our stomachs and laughing, until we got to the bleachers and collapsed against them, laughing even harder. Once we both caught our breath, we talked about how awful dodgeball is, and the possibility that Mr. Skinner is actually a robot or an alien from outer space. Eventually, we just sat there looking up at the clouds and laughing at the shapes we saw: a sheep; a face; a heart. I remember feeling weirdly aware of how close my hand was to Tina's on the warm metal bleachers.

It was by far the most fun I've ever had with a girl, until we got caught. Mrs. O'Dell appeared out of nowhere and startled us both by shouting, "Joe Roadsteen! Tina Brown! Aren't you two supposed to be at Gym?" Instead of making us go back, she made us follow her to her office where she wrote us both one-week detention slips we had to bring home to our parents.

Mom was mad, but I don't regret any of it because I got to spend so much time with Tina that week... even if it was silent time in detention, sitting at separate desks, alternating between homework and staring at the clock. We'd turn and smile at each other occasionally, and I'd try not to laugh thinking about the great dodgeball escape and how it felt to have my hand so close to hers on those bleachers.

Since then, I have developed quite the crush on Tina. I can't help but look over at her all the time when we're in math class, and I think about her a lot when we're not at school together.

The semi-formal's two weeks away, and I can't imagine going with anyone other than Tina. I don't even talk to any other girls. So, I've decided, today is the day I'm going to ask her to the dance.

How should I do it? I've thought about writing her a note and squeezing it through the metal slats of her locker. Marcy is Tina's best friend, and I've thought about asking her if she thinks Tina would say yes if I asked her. But when I think about all these things, they make me feel more nervous. I should ask. What's the worst thing that could happen?

When Tina got to third-period math class, I was already there. She smiled and waved to me. But then she sat down at her desk, turned around, and the bell rang before I could go over to her. So, I decided to do it at lunch. I sat at my usual table, half listening to Tom and Brian talk about the plot to some movie they saw, but mostly watching the entrance to the cafeteria, waiting for Tina. For some reason, she never appeared. She must've had a class project or a lunch group today. I was so distracted, I forgot to eat my pizza and had to stuff the whole piece into my mouth when the bell rang.

For the rest of the day, I didn't bump into Tina at all. All day, I heard rumors about who asked who to the dance. Skylar asked Ryder, and he said yes, obviously; they're pretty much a couple. Jamie asked Gina who also said yes, and I've never even seen them talk to each other! It felt like everyone was talking about the dance (other than Tom and Brian who will definitely stay home and play video games instead). I started to feel anxious as the school day came to an end, and I still hadn't seen Tina.

Eventually, the final bell rang, and I went to my locker to pack up my things. I was still thinking about Tina as I closed my locker; and when I slammed it shut, there she was, standing right on the other side of my locker door, staring me right in the eye. My heart thudded in my chest.

"Whoa," I said, startled.

"Hey," she said, calmly.

"Hey," I said, trying to be cool and keep my smile from becoming as big as it wanted to be.

There was a long pause. I was trying to figure out exactly what to say... *Will you go to the dance with me?* – or, would it be better to make some small-talk first? But before I could decide, Tina said, "Are you going to ask me or not?"

"What?" I said, surprised. Was she reading my mind? "I mean... yeah." I cleared my throat and looked down at my shoes. "Will you go to the dance with me?" I looked up to meet her eyes, and she was smiling.

"Took you long enough," she said. "Yes, I'll go to the dance with you, Joe." Instantly, I let my smile be as big as it wanted to be. It felt like there was a little kid in my chest, jumping up and down shouting, *she likes me too, she likes me too, she likes me too!*

With newfound confidence, I decided to press my luck. "Um, also," I started, "if you want to come over on Saturday, that would be cool. I have a basketball hoop." *I have a basketball hoop? I have a basketball hoop?? What kind of thing is that to say?* This is exactly why I don't talk to girls.

"Sure, that sounds fun," she said, easily.

## JOURNEY TAKEAWAYS:

✓ This chapter reminds us life still goes on. If someone in your family has Alzheimer's or dementia, or if your family is dealing with some other kind of stress, it does not mean you should stop living.

✓ It is important to keep doing things that make you happy. Many people call this "self-care." Caring for yourself by making plans to do fun things is a good way to relieve stress and keep yourself healthy.

✓ New friendships are very important, as are old friendships. The more friends you have around, the stronger your support system, and the stronger you will feel.

# CHAPTER
## 6

# Babysitting Grandma

**W**hen Saturday rolls around, I am so excited I can't even sleep late like I usually do. I wake up at 8am, take a shower, comb my hair, brush my teeth, and try on three different shirts. Tina's supposed to be here around noon. We'll probably order pizza, and thanks to my brilliant advertising of the basketball hoop, I guess we'll play some games, like H.O.R.S.E. or Knock Out, until we get bored.

Tina arrives in a light blue shirt and jeans. I see her walking up the street from my attic window, and I race down the two flights of stairs to be the first to open the door. Fortunately, Emily's not home, and Dad took Bentley to a birthday party.

I still want to get there before Mom does. I go as fast as I can, and success! I'm the first one there. I take a second to catch my breath, smooth my hair, and open the door before Tina even rings the doorbell.

"Hey," she says, a little startled. It's like when she surprised me at my locker, except now the tables have turned.

"Hey," I say. "Come in."

I give Tina a little tour around the house, pointing out the living room and the bathroom. Mom said we're not supposed to hang out in my room, so I only show her the attic for a minute, but when she looks around, she says, "Wow, this is so cool. I can't believe you have a whole floor to yourself!" I silently thank Grandma once again for my unexpectedly awesome new room.

We walk back downstairs to the kitchen.

"Want some iced tea?" I ask.

"Sure," Tina says. I'm pouring her a glass when Grandma walks in.

"Hello," she says to Tina, staring at her for a long few seconds before turning to me and saying, "Richard, who's your pretty friend?"

Richard is my uncle's name.

> When a person with dementia confuses you with someone else, it is often another family member or someone who you look like.

I look at Tina and see the confusion on her face as she tilts her head to one side and squints a little bit. I wonder if she thinks I have a secret identity and my real name is actually Richard.

I probably should have warned Tina that Grandma has Alzheimer's disease, but I didn't think of it. Oh well. I speak slowly and clearly as I've become so used to doing. "Grandma, I'm Joseph. This is my friend, Tina." Grandma looks at Tina again, and Tina smiles and says, "Hi."

Turning back to me, Grandma asks, "Are you taking my daughter on a date?"

"No, Grandma," I blush a little at hearing the word *date* in Tina's presence, and I wonder what the heck Tina must be thinking. Grandma probably sounds insane.

I think about how I could try to make Grandma understand the situation in as few words as possible, but I know anything I say right now will probably just confuse her more.

Mom says sometimes we just need to join Grandma in whatever she's saying and try to avoid correcting her. This, Mom says, "is a way of living in Grandma's reality." So, I decide not to press the issue. If Grandma wants to call me Richard or thinks Tina is her daughter, there's really no harm in that. Correcting her might just make her feel more confused and frustrated.

But Tina still looks a little bit confused herself, which is totally understandable. I pass her the glass of iced tea and give her the same nod toward the back door as she gave me that day we escaped from dodgeball.

"We're going outside, Grandma!"

"Okay, Rich," she says as Tina and I escape to the backyard.

"Sorry about that," I say to Tina once we're outside. "That must've seemed pretty weird. My grandma has dementia." I look at Tina to see how she'll respond. I suddenly realize how much I've gotten used to Grandma, and how much the stuff she says and does has started to become kind of normal to me. It wasn't very long ago that I didn't even know what the word "dementia" meant.

"That's okay," Tina says, "I get it. My great-aunt had Alzheimer's disease."

Dementia affects many families, so don't be surprised if someone you know is going through the same thing. And if someone doesn't know what dementia is, don't be afraid to tell them. It is important to share your knowledge.

"Wow," I say, feeling relieved, and a little excited we have something big in common. "It's crazy right?"

"Yeah it is," Tina says, picking up the basketball and giving it two quick bounces on the pavement. She squints at the hoop, bends her knees, and arcs a perfect shot straight into the basket – swoosh, nothing but net.

Half an hour later, we go back inside to order a pizza, and Mom's on the phone, pacing back and forth in the kitchen.

Apparently, Josie's Diner is on the phone and they're asking her to come in today. Either Mom's got the volume turned way up or her manager is shouting because I can hear every word of the phone call. Two of the other servers called in sick, and now they're down to two people, which is not nearly enough people on a busy Saturday.

Mom holds up her index finger to me – the universal sign for "wait a minute" and then she notices Tina. Her face softens, and she wiggles her fingers in a little wave.

"I hear what you're saying, Trish, but I'm home with my mother today; you know I can't leave her." Trish's response is quieter this time. I can't understand what she's saying, but judging by the look on Mom's face, I can tell Trish still isn't letting her off the hook easily.

Lately, Mom looks like she's been getting less and less sleep. Not to be rude but she looks a little bit like a zombie. She has dark circles under her eyes, and I'm pretty sure she's lost weight. "Okay," Mom says, "okay... Let me see if there's anything I can do... okay... I'll call you back... bye."

Mom hangs up the phone and breathes a heavy sigh. "Hi!" she says to Tina, trying to brighten her expression. "I'm Joe's mom. Call me Jeanette." Mom holds out her hand.

Tina shakes it and says, "I'm Tina."

"That sounded like a fun phone call," I say to Mom, sarcastically.

"You're right, it wasn't. Trish needs me to come into Josie's this afternoon but your dad's not home, and I obviously can't leave Grandma. I guess I could call Mary and see if she could possibly come over, but—"

Suddenly, I get a brilliant idea. It's perfect. Nobody home except Grandma and Grandpa? And Tina? I take the ideal opportunity to look like a real gentleman in front of Tina.

"I can watch Grandma if you need me to," I say nonchalantly as if this is something I do all the time.

Mom looks surprised and impressed. She looks from me, to Tina, then back to me. I can tell she wants to say yes, but she pauses. "Are you sure, Joe? That's a lot of responsibility."

It seems like Mom trusts me to do this, but she doesn't want to burden me. And, I can imagine nothing better than being pretty much home alone with Tina, so I reassure her I'm capable and I don't mind watching Grandma.

"Oh, my goodness, you're awesome, Joe!" Mom says, gratefully, taking my face in both hands and giving me a big kiss on the cheek.

"Mom!" I exclaim, mortified for her to kiss me in front of Tina. Tina giggles as Mom apologizes and uses her thumb to smudge some lipstick off my cheek.

Mom immediately gets into go-mode, hunting inside her wallet for a $20 bill, which she puts on the counter and tells us to buy pizza with. She pauses, then slaps another $20 down. Sweet!

She starts to go over some rules, but all I hear is *blah, blah, blah... watch Grandma.* I'm too excited for Mom to leave so we can eat junk food and watch TV. Mom points to the list of emergency contacts on the refrigerator. The one number she has highlighted is for the local Alzheimer's Support Center.

"You can always call them if anything happens. Or, just call me at the diner. I can be back in 10 minutes if you need me." I say *okay*, but I can't imagine what could go wrong. "Grandma and Grandpa ate an hour ago, so they're all set for lunch. Dad should be home around 4, so he'll do dinner, and I'll be at Josie's through the dinner rush."

"Okay, Mom," I say, calmly, "don't worry. I've got this."

"I'm sorry to run out," Mom says, "but I'm glad I finally got to meet the famous Tina!"

"Mom!!!" I protest, blushing hard. Tina smiles and raises her eyebrows at me.

"Sorry! Okay! I'm leaving!" Mom grabs her purse and rushes out the front door already on the phone with Trish to say she's on her way to save the day.

So. Here we are. I'm in charge of the house, and I am practically alone in it with the incredible Tina Brown.

"So," I say to Tina. "This is cool. But, it's also kind of weird... My grandma always used to babysit me when I was little, and now I guess we're babysitting her."

Tina looks at me sympathetically, then picks the $40 up from the counter and makes a crazy face. "Let's order all of the pizza, mwahaha!" she says, and we both start laughing uncontrollably.

An hour later, Tina and I are sitting in the living room eating pizza, garlic knots, and washing it down with rivers of soda, when Grandma walks in and asks to use the bathroom. I get up and show her where it is even though she has obviously used it a million times before. I know how bad her memory is, and sometimes she gets turned around inside the house. Also, Mom says some of the medication Grandma takes makes her feel like she has to go to the bathroom all the time. That sounds so annoying. It makes me sad for Grandma. I hope none of this stuff happens to me when I get old.

"I'm back!" I say to Tina, sitting down next to her on the couch. Within minutes, we're watching YouTube videos on her phone and laughing uncontrollably again. Considering this is the first time we've really hung out outside of school, it's pretty amazing that we get along so well. Every few minutes I turn from the cat videos to Tina and notice the cute way her nose wrinkles when she smiles.

She catches me looking at her and says, "what?" through her laughter.

I think about telling her how pretty she is, but Grandma comes back into the room.

"I think I'll take a nap now," she announces, shuffling across the floor in front of us to her favorite chair right next to the couch. Grandpa Ben is probably snoring away upstairs, too. They both usually take naps after lunch.

"Great idea, Grandma," I say, watching her get comfortable and close her eyes. Tina takes a blanket off the arm of the couch, walks over to Grandma, and drapes it gently over her lap, which is about the nicest thing I think I've ever seen. Within minutes, Grandma is snoring.

"Want to hang out in my room?" I ask Tina. "I don't know if you noticed, but I have an incredibly sweet TV."

"Do you think that's a good idea?" Tina says, providing a voice of reason. "We're supposed to watch your Grandma."

"Oh yeah," I say, "don't worry. She's not going anywhere." Grandma always takes long naps in the afternoon, and I'll leave the attic door open, so we'll hear what's going on.

"Okay," Tina says, and we walk up to the attic.

I sit cross-legged on the end of my bed and Tina keeps her left foot on the floor, crossing her right leg over her left and leaning on one elbow, reclined but reserved and at least two feet away from me. I scroll through the movie menu and we pick something funny since laughing is quite clearly our theme of the day. Within half an hour, we're both relaxed and absorbed by the movie.

Then, Tina turns to me. I turn to Tina, and we both stare at each other with relaxed expressions, while in my mind I'm freaking out. Is this it? My first kiss? I summon some courage, inhale deeply, and smell the unmistakable smell of... something burning! It dawns on me it's coming from the kitchen. Grandma is cooking.

"Oh no," Tina says, smelling it, too. We both get to our feet, and I run down the stairs as Tina follows closely behind. We pass my old room, and I glance in to see that Grandpa is still napping soundly. I don't wake him; we keep running.

As I'm coming down the stairs, I notice the air a little bit white with smoke, and it's definitely coming from the kitchen. Tina and I run into the kitchen, and I turn off the

JOINING GRANDMA'S JOURNEY

oven. Tina shouts, "Quick! Open some windows before the smoke alarm goes off!" We both race around the kitchen opening every window. I run into the living room to grab the empty pizza box and start fanning smoke out of the back door, when suddenly it dawns on me... where is Grandma?

"Tina, she's not in the living room!" I shout. "Can you check the first floor?" I run back upstairs to look in Mom and Dad's room, Emily's room, Bentley's room, one last check in on Grandpa who is definitely alone in there — still snoring — and then the upstairs bathroom. Grandma is nowhere to be seen.

My heart is pounding. I run back downstairs and look at Tina, who shakes her head "no" and looks pale as a ghost. "Grandma Mae!" I yell, opening the front door. Maybe's she's gone outside to sit on the porch. But no, she's not there. As I continue to panic, my imagination goes crazy. I can already see the newspaper headline: *Grandson left to watch Grandma almost lets the house burn down and loses Grandma.* Mom is going to kill me.

"Grandma Mae, where are you!?"

I run out to the street and look both ways. I have no idea what I should do. "Should we call the Alzheimer's Support Center, like your mom said?" Tina's a genius.

"Yes. Can you go outside and see if you see her? I'll call."

"Okay," Tina says, giving me a hug before she goes. Even though I didn't think my heart could beat any faster, it skips a beat when Tina hugs me.

I look at the number on the fridge and carefully punch it into our kitchen phone.

A cheerful voice answers, "Alzheimer's Support Center, this is Becky, how may I help you?"

"Hi, my name's Joseph, and I... I think I lost my grandmother." I explain the situation: Grandma has Alzheimer's; she was taking a nap one minute, and the next minute there was smoke in the kitchen and she was gone. "I can't find her anywhere! I'm freaking out!"

"Slow down, Honey. Take a big, deep breath for me," Becky soothes, and I do as she says. "It's common for folks with Alzheimer's to wander away sometimes. Try not to panic. Do you know which hand is your grandma's dominant hand?"

"What does that mean?" I ask.

"The hand she writes with," Becky explains.

I don't know why she would ask that, but I've always thought it was kind of cool that Grandma is left-handed, so I happen to know the answer. Becky tells me to go outside and walk in that direction. "People with dementia usually wander in the direction of their dominant hand," Becky explains. "Walk about 10 minutes in that direction and see if you find her. If you don't, call me right back, and I can contact the local police department for you. We can send out a group of volunteers to help you look for her, okay Hon?"

"Okay! Thank you!" I say, hanging up the phone without saying goodbye. Woops. I think she'll understand. I head outside and see Tina walking around from the backyard.

"I checked around back," she said. "She's not there."

"She might have gone this way!" I say, pointing left. "But can you wait here in case she shows up?" I say, jogging backwards to face Tina until she says yes. As soon as she does, I call out a thank you into the wind as

71

I quickly turn around and start running as fast as I can.

After about 5 minutes, which feel like forever, I'm about to give up and turn around when I notice someone walking a little further up the road. I run faster, and when I get closer, I see that it's Grandma.

Sprinting up to her, I can't help but immediately blurt out, "Thank God, I found you! Grandma, where are you going?" She's startled at first, but turns to me and smiles as if nothing out of the ordinary is happening at all.

"Oh, Joe!" she says, recognizing me instantly. "I needed an egg for the brownies and I couldn't find the car keys."

> Dementia symptoms can come and go. Sometimes someone may be very confused; other times they seem completely normal. Sometimes they forget and confuse names, other times they are able to recognize a friendly face or even recall a name they couldn't remember a few minutes before.

I think about correcting her – reminding her that she can't drive anymore because she has Alzheimer's, and that she's not supposed to leave the house by herself. Then

JOINING GRANDMA'S JOURNEY

I remember what Mom always says: try to join her on her journey; meet her where she is; respect her reality. So instead of correcting her, I redirect her.

I try a little white lie. "Ohh, okay, Grandma, but the store's the other way. Let me help you. Let's turn around." I point her back in the direction of the house. As we walk, I slowly change the subject. We talk about the nice weather and the flowers on the trees we walk by – slowly, at Grandma's pace. I text Tina "FOUND HER" so she's not left there worrying.

After a few minutes, I ask to hold the plastic shopping bags Grandma has balled up in one hand. She gives them to me and I casually stuff them in my back pocket in an effort to put shopping out of her mind. When we arrive back at the house, she walks right inside with me without any further mention of going to the store.

I have to say, I have no idea what I would have done if it was not for Becky at the Alzheimer's Support Center telling me to go left. I'm so glad I called, and I make a mental note of the lesson: people with dementia wander in the direction of their dominant hand... and never leave Grandma alone.

I settle Grandma back into her favorite chair, then look around for Tina. Before I leave the living room, she emerges from the kitchen. She sees Grandma and we both share a long stare of relief and disbelief. "I'm so glad you found her!" Tina whispers.

"Me too." I say, stepping with her into the kitchen. "Thank you for keeping watch. I'm sorry about that."

"Don't be sorry. All's well that ends well!" Tina is wise beyond her years. "I think I better get going," she says, "let you guys have some time together. I'll see you at school?" I'm disappointed our hangout has to end, but she's probably right — enough excitement for one day.

"Okay," I say, and I hug her. She hugs me back and we share a smile.

"See ya, Joe," says Tina as she shows herself out the front door.

I sit down on the couch next to Grandma's chair. "You ready to do some baking?"

Her face lights up. I check the fridge for eggs, and sure enough, we have a dozen in the fridge. I turn the radio to Grandma's favorite oldies station and open her old recipe binder. The book is worn at the edges, the pages splotched with ingredients from decades of use. Together, we bake a perfect batch of brownies.

> A person with dementia will surprise you. Try to encourage them to keep doing the things they have always loved. Often, those are the activities they are able to keep doing for the longest time.

I used to be the one to help Grandma. Now, I lead and she follows. But, if I give her simple jobs to do — pour in the chocolate chips, stir the batter — and if I wait patiently, I see that Grandma completes each task happily. Clearly glad to take part in a beloved, familiar activity, she smells and feels all the ingredients at every step, smiling.

Before we call upstairs to Grandpa to wake up and share some brownies, I call Becky at the Alzheimer's Center back to let her know that everything turned out fine. I tell her I don't know what I would have done without her. She says, "that's what I'm here for, honey."

When Mom comes home, she sees me, Grandma, and Grandpa sitting on the front porch eating brownies and drinking iced tea. She gives me a kiss on the head and tells me I'm amazing.

"Thank you for being my wonderful grown-up son," she says. "I'm proud of you, Joe." I know I should confess and tell Mom everything that happened, but in this moment, I can't bear to have her pride in me disappear. The good news: Grandma has totally forgotten what happened, and she's home safe and sound. I feel guilty, but I take a bite of brownie and say nothing.

"Brownies, too?" Mom says, genuinely surprised.

"They're so good," I say with a gooey, chocolatey mouthful. Mom laughs, Grandma and Grandpa smile, and all's well that ends well.

The next weekend, Dad's helping me tie my tie and get ready for the semi-formal.

"You excited for this, bud?" he asks.

"I am," I admit.

"Well, good. You just remember to be a gentleman, and call me when you guys need a ride home. You ready?"

"Yeah," I say, and we head downstairs together. Dad's taking me to pick up Tina in his '57 Chevy. I'm pretty excited about that because I know the rest of the kids will probably get dropped off in their parents' ordinary cars and minivans. Sure enough, when Tina opens the door, she smiles at me – and she smiles at the car, too.

"We're going in that?" she asks, wide-eyed.

"Yeah we are!" I say. "Also, you look really nice," I say, nervously. She does. She's wearing a purple dress and she's got a white flower in her hair.

She blushes a little. "Thanks, Joe," she says, taking my arm. "Bye, Mom!" she calls inside as she starts to close the door.

"Wait!" I hear a voice yell from inside. Tina's mom runs out with her phone in her hand. "Pictures!!!" she says. "You must be Joseph," she says, shaking my hand, "and that is one beautiful car!"

My dad gets out to introduce himself to Tina's mom. He lets us pose next to the Chevy. I don't usually like getting my picture taken, but I have a feeling I'll be glad to have this one.

We say goodbye to Tina's mom again and climb into the backseat of Dad's car. He's on his best behavior – just driving, no talking, like I asked.

"How's your crazy Gram?" she says, and I get a little nervous she'll talk about what happened. Obviously, Dad doesn't know. But before I even answer, Tina says, "I like her, she's super cute."

"She likes you, too," I say, but I'm definitely not talking about Grandma. I have the biggest crush on Tina Brown. She smiles and looks out the window, which is open. The gentle breeze is blowing through her hair as Dad drives slowly, taking us the long way from Tina's house to school.

When we arrive, I say, "hold on!" and jump out to open the door for Tina like Dad does for Mom on special occasions.

"Thanks," she says, and holds my hand as she gets out. She keeps holding it as I close the car door, and she keeps holding it as we walk in together. Me, Tina, the car, the dance. I'm loving this moment so much that I forget to say bye to Dad. But he gets it. I glance back before we head in, and Dad's still waiting there, just like Mom does. He gives me a thumbs-up and slowly pulls the car back onto the road toward home. I turn back toward Tina and the front doors to the gym, which are decorated with posters for the dance.

When we open the doors, the gym lights are off and the whole place is covered with colored lights, streamers, and paper lanterns. I'm not big on sentimental things, but to be honest, it looks like heaven.

## JOURNEY TAKEAWAYS:

✓ Do not be afraid to introduce new people to someone with dementia and to educate others about dementia. New experiences are good for the brain.

✓ As dementia progresses, it is common for people to wander. Remember that they may wander in the direction of their dominant hand. Remember to call the Alzheimer's Support Center right away whenever you need help.

✓ You can keep your loved one safer by putting a card with their information in their pocket and knowing where they might want to go.

✓ In this chapter, Joseph made a few mistakes that could have had dangerous consequences. When you make a mistake, admit it. It is very important to be honest. Remember that you are part of a team. Joseph should tell his parents that Grandma tried to use the oven and wandered away because it will help them all prepare for the possibility of these things happening again.

*In the next chapter, you will learn how color and a person's home environment can affect how they behave.*

# CHAPTER
## 7

# Trapped Inside

**"C**ome on, Mom,"* my mother says to Grandma over and over, again and again, like a broken record. For some reason, my grandma refuses to leave the house today. It's been several weeks since the last time she went out.

Even Grandpa really prefers to stay inside lately. He likes to be where Grandma is. We've tried everything to make them come on some errands with us. When

Grandma refused to go to her doctor's appointment, Mom told her they were going to the antique store. Grandma said, "Why would I go shopping? I have everything I need." We've tried to get her to go to the grocery store, but she says it's too cold in there. Dad even tried bribing her with a $5 bill, but she said, "Don't be silly; I'm fine right here."

Grandma doesn't even sit on the porch anymore like she used to. Mostly, she just sits in the same armchair all day. She must have gained 20 pounds since she stopped going places with us. She still likes to eat, but now she barely moves. It's strange, but when she looks in the mirror, it doesn't seem like she really recognizes herself because in her mind, she's still a different version of herself.

Fed up, and running out of ideas, Mom called her friend Mary, who referred us to someone at the Senior Center who knows a lot about dementia. Mom finally decided to go to a local support group, and she came home with lots of new information. We learned we could get Grandma to eat less by putting her food on a smaller, dark blue plate. It seems silly, but hey, whatever works!

Most cities and towns have support groups that can provide you with information about dementia. Just Google "Dementia support groups near me" to find some options.

We've also learned that many different colors can influence Grandma's behavior (hence the dark blue plates). Red plates, for example, can increase appetite and make you want to eat more. That must be why so many fast-food containers are red!

Each morning, Grandma walks into the kitchen while my sisters and I are eating breakfast. One morning, I notice that every time she passed the kitchen trashcan, she flinches, almost like she's seen a ghost or a mouse. Once I notice this, I decide to do an experiment. I move the trashcan to the other side of the kitchen, and it's like magic! The next time she walks by, she doesn't flinch.

Next experiment: I put the trashcan in the living room, right behind her favorite chair, and I wait and watch to see what she'll do. Sure enough, when she sees it, she flinches; and for the rest of the day, she sits in the kitchen instead of in her favorite chair.

The experimentation continues. My science teacher would be proud! I replace the kitchen trashcan with the one from the upstairs bathroom, which is white with little flowers on it. The next morning, she doesn't flinch when she walks by that trashcan, so I guess it wasn't garbage that was scaring her. I shrug my shoulders, put the trashcans back in their proper places, and take some time to figure out the mystery.

The next day, when Grandma walks into the kitchen, I see she once again flinches when she sees the regular kitchen trashcan, and it was like a lightbulb turned on in my head. The kitchen trashcan is black. The bathroom trashcan is white. Maybe it has something to do with color!

So, the kitchen trashcan is black, and she wasn't afraid of the white one. Could she be scared of the color black? *Well, let's see,* I think. *If I put a black t-shirt on the floor in the kitchen, let's see if she'll walk by it.*

"Why is this shirt on the floor?" says Emily the next morning.

"Shhhh!" I scold her. "It's an experiment!"

"Whatever, freak," she says, sitting down at the table and pouring some cereal.

My cereal's getting soggy because I've been waiting for Grandma for so long. Finally, she comes down the stairs, and I watch her like a hawk. She shuffles into the kitchen and sees the shirt. She stops and doesn't pass. In fact, she turns around and walks away.

"Grandma!" I call after her, abandoning my soggy cereal with excitement. "I want to show you something!"

I go and get her from the living room and walk her back into the kitchen. We're standing right next to the t-shirt and once again, she stops in her tracks. "Come on," I say, "it's right out the back door."

Grandma lifts one leg and tries to take a big step over the t-shirt, holding my arm and leaning on me hard. But, she chickens out and puts her foot back down on the floor.

"No, I don't want to go outside," she says. "Not in the mood."

I reach down, pick up the t-shirt, and throw it across the room. "Please, Grandma? It'll only take a second." I invite her to walk to the back door again. She studies the floor again, and I notice an expression of relief on her face. Like magic, she walks right by without hesitating. My hypothesis is confirmed: I really think she's afraid of the color black!

I'm too excited to even explain what I'm doing. I race to the front door and look down at the welcome mat. Just as I thought, it's black.

> Different colors can mean different things to people with dementia. The color black is often scary to them when it is on the floor. For example, a dark-colored rug can look like a large hole, and a black trashcan can look like an animal or another confusing presence.

I throw the welcome mat off the front porch and call to her. "Come on, Grandma, the weather's beautiful today!"

It's like I'm trying to lure a rabbit with a carrot. She comes to meet me at the front door, looks down, and walks right out onto the front porch. For the first time in a long time, she sits on the rocking chair we brought from her house, and I hear her breathe a sigh of relief.

"Mom!" I yell into the house.

She calls back, "What?" with irritation like I'm asking her to watch me blow bubbles in my chocolate milk (again).

"Come quick! It's Grandma!" I shout, and predictably, Mom comes running. When she sees Grandma on the porch, smiling and watching the birds, Mom puts her hand over her mouth in astonishment and looks unbelievably happy. She gives me a hug, and whispers, "how did you do that?" Then she turns to Grandma and says, "You enjoying the weather, Mom?"

And Grandma says, "I sure am, Jeanie. I sure am."

With the welcome mat gone, we no longer have trouble getting Grandma to go outside. She comes on little shopping trips and walks again. The fresh air and exercise really seem to be good for her.

The whole experience makes me wonder why she's scared of the color black. I find the stack of pamphlets Mom brought home from the support group and find one called Your Living Environment. It has a section about color, and I learn that black objects can basically look like giant black holes to Grandma. Maybe she was afraid to fall in.

I wonder how other colors might be affecting Grandma and I read the whole rest of the pamphlet. It's so funny how a tiny change has improved her daily life so much. I am so happy I could help her get outside again. I never thought that throwing away a welcome mat could make me feel so proud.

## JOURNEY TAKEAWAYS:

✓ Objects in your home can have an effect on how someone with dementia behaves. In this chapter, Joseph's grandma is scared to cross the black welcome mat, and that prevents her from wanting to go outside.

✓ Kids are some of the most curious people on earth, which can be very helpful. Use your natural creativity and your ability to learn quickly to discover ways to help your loved one be more successful.

✓ Remember that there is always support available. Most people who work with those who have dementia are happy to explain things or help you solve problems.

*In the next chapter, you will learn about another helpful technique for a common problem.*

# CHAPTER 8

# Hoarding Drawers and the Missing Remote

"*W*here's the remote control!?" I say as I flip the cushions off of the couch and onto the living room floor. All I find is loose change, a paperclip, and a squished piece of popcorn. I take the coins and put them in my pocket and yell, "Mom, the TV remote is nowhere to be found!"

"Look under the couch!" she calls from the other room.

"I already did!"

"What about on the shelves by the TV?"

"I looked there! I'm telling you, it's nowhere!" I put the couch back together and sit on it, beginning to lose interest in watching television anyway. I decide to ride my bike instead. Later, Mom changes Grandma and Grandpa's sheets and finds the remote under the pillows.

A few days later, Emily is looking for her cell phone. She's freaking out about it, obviously, because her phone is basically her life. After about an hour she actually starts to cry, and convinces everyone to help her look.

Eventually, we find Emily's phone in my Grandma's top dresser drawer. After we find it, I realize something interesting: Emily's phone case is purple. I spontaneously remember the pamphlet about colors said purple is a color of valuable things people with dementia often like to collect. I gotta say, the more I learn about this whole color thing, the more I'm fascinated by it.

Later that month, Dad couldn't find his wallet, and by then we knew where to look. Guess where we found it? Grandma's room. Mom's address book? Grandma's room. More and more frequently, it became clear Grandma was stealing our stuff!

You may think this is stealing, but most of the time, people with dementia tend to take items because they think they belong to them or because the objects make them feel safe.

Mom says this behavior is called hoarding, and it's common for people with dementia. I've never heard of hoarding, so I look it up and learn it's a term used to describe when people gather and keep items they don't really need. Mom says when people develop dementia, they often start collecting things to feel safe. Maybe they lived through a time when they did not have much, so they learned to hold onto everything they could. Or, maybe they feel their memories slipping away, so they try to hold onto what they can: objects. I guess it makes sense.

As Grandma's hoarding gets worse, Mom makes another appointment with her doctor. We ask what we can do to help manage this habit. It's pretty amazing to me that someone would go to school for that long to become a doctor, but the more I learn about this stuff, the more I think I might like to be a doctor someday, too.

At the appointment, the doctor tells Mom about *hoarding drawers.* None of us have any idea what those are. The idea is to take the top drawer of Grandma's dresser, empty it out, and fill it with items she loves to look at and tinker with. Apparently, this will help her create a habit of putting special things in this location. Then, when she takes something, she will most likely put it in that drawer. And when something goes missing, hopefully it will be easier for us to find it.

"Hoarding drawers work for a lot of people with dementia," the doctor says, "but I can't promise it'll work for everyone." At this point, anything is worth trying.

We go home and get right to work. Mom asks me to entertain Grandma while she creates the new hoarding drawer. It's nice to see Mom's face full of hope. You can see that sparkle of hope in her face each time she tries out a solution to one of these problems. We have that in common.

I think Mom feels good that she has a chance to make things a little better for Grandma. Mom would never say this outloud, but at this point, we have all come to understand Grandma is not going to get better. Not all the way better. In fact, judging by the way things have been going, things will probably even get worse. But if we can make life better for Grandma in the meantime, then that's what we'll try our very best to do.

Once the drawer is set up, Mom calls for a family meeting to ensure we are all on the same page. Grandma's in her armchair, but the rest of us gather around the dining room table. I look around at Grandpa, Dad, Mom, Emily, and Bentley. I listen as Mom confidently takes control and explains to everyone how the hoarding drawer is going to work. We are a team.

A few weeks later, we are all in the habit of checking the drawer for items when they go missing. Guess what? We're lucky. It works! Every time some little object goes missing, we check the drawer, and there it is!

## JOURNEY TAKEAWAY:

✓ Remember that if your loved one develops a habit of hoarding or taking things, they are not intentionally stealing the items to hurt or annoy you. It makes Joseph's grandma feel good to collect special things. In this chapter, we saw how a hoarding drawer helped their family find the missing objects.

✓ This chapter also shows the importance of putting potentially dangerous items, such as sharp knives, harmful cleaning products, and medication, somewhere that a person with dementia cannot get them, such as in a locked drawer or cabinet. If someone with dementia is in your house, work with a responsible adult to make sure the house is safe.

✓ Joseph's family is facing the reality that Grandma's condition is never going to go away completely. They can't control that, so instead, they are controlling what they can control. They are learning from their experiences and working as a team to make life a little easier for everyone, which is the best that anyone can do.

# CHAPTER
## 9

# The Holiday Dinner

*I*t's Thanksgiving, which means the time has come for our whole family to come together. Aunt Rita, Uncle Dave, and the kids live about four hours away so we only see them around the holidays. This is the first year that Thanksgiving is going to be at our new house! It's usually at Grandma and Grandpa's.

As the smell of the special holiday food fills the kitchen, family arrives and the house fills up in a happy, crowded way. Emily plays DJ, putting on music through the speakers, and everyone seems comfortable – talking and laughing with each other. Even though Grandma cannot lead with the cooking like she used to, she seems happy just sitting at the kitchen counter, listening to the music, watching the kids run around and the grown-ups all pitch in to prepare the meal.

Mom asks Grandma if she'd like a cup of coffee. Grandma nods. She drinks one cup. A little while later, I notice my aunt pouring her another; and later, I see my uncle refilling her mug again. I don't think too much about it, but I do notice that all Grandma's doing is sitting there while people pour her more coffee. *How much coffee can one person drink?* I wonder, but coffee's gross and I've never had more than a sip or two, so what do I know?

> Often, a person with dementia may compulsively drink or forget they just drank something. As a family, try to keep track of what and how much the person drinks, especially caffeinated beverages.

When it comes time to eat, everyone sits down at the dining room table. There's

JOINING GRANDMA'S JOURNEY

an enormous spread of special holiday food, a big centerpiece, and Dad lights two tall red candles to signify the start of the meal. I look around the table and do not see Grandma. Mom and I share a look, and she asks me to find Grandma for dinner, so I do. My cousin, Kate, says she saw Grandma walking up the stairs just a few minutes ago. So, I go upstairs and knock on her door.

There's no answer. I knock again, and in a few moments, she comes to the door. She seems frantic, and all of her clothes are pulled out of her drawers and onto the floor. "What's going on, Grandma?" I say, calmly and gently. "Can I help you?"

At this point, her speech is not very good. She doesn't usually talk very much because she has so much difficulty getting her words out. As Grandma walks away from me, I notice her pants are wet. She sees me notice and starts to cry. Tears run down her face, and my heart breaks.

> It is common for a person with dementia to lose the ability to control their bladder. Sometimes, they just don't make it to the bathroom in time. This is called "incontinence."

She starts trying to speak in that strange

Aphasia language I do not understand. She's piecing words together that don't make sense, and she just seems so confused. Her inability to explain herself makes her frustrated. I can tell she wants privacy but I also know she needs my help.

My feelings take over, and my body starts to shake a little bit. I'm not sure what to say or do, and it's so sad to see her this way. Downstairs, I hear everyone talking and laughing. I don't want to interrupt the party with this news, and I don't want to embarrass Grandma. Mom yells up the stairs "Everything okay, Joe?"

I yell back, "Yeah, I've got it! We'll be there in a minute!"

I know it would kill my Mom to see Grandma like this. I know that Grandma's ability to make it to the bathroom on her own is a pretty important life skill, and it scares me to think this skill might be slipping away from her.

I take a big, deep breath and think to myself: if I were in Grandma's shoes, I wouldn't want everyone to know what happened. I would just want someone to help me and reassure me everything was okay. So, I say to Grandma, "Don't worry, it could happen to anyone."

She looks at me and smiles because she knows I am there to help her. But just in case, I say out loud, "I'm here to help you."

I grab her bathrobe and drape it around her shoulders. I go to her dresser and take out some new clothes for her to wear. I lay them out on the bed and turn around as I hand her each piece of clothing in the correct order so she puts them on correctly. She slowly gets changed, and puts the dirty clothes in the hamper on her own. I tell her, "It's okay. All better now."

> Remember that it is always okay to ask for help. You do not need to do anything that makes you feel uncomfortable.

Grandma smiles and kisses my forehead. My heart breaks a little more. I know I will never forget this moment, but I am glad that Grandma will.

We go to the bathroom and wash our hands before we walk downstairs. I help Grandma to her seat next to Mom where her food is placed and already cut up for her.

I go and sit at my place on the other side of the table. Grandma looks over at me and smiles. Maybe she has already forgotten how exactly I helped her, but clearly she knows how much I love her.

Dad raises his glass to make a toast. "Happy Thanksgiving, everybody. I'm so glad we're all together again this year. It's been a tough one, but we're getting through it together. I just want to take a second to honor Jeanette," Dad says, turning to Mom. His eyes are glinting in the candlelight. "You amaze me, sweetheart. Thank you for being the glue that holds all of this together. Now, let's eat!"

"Here, here!" Uncle Dave exclaims.

"Salud!" Grandpa Ben says, raising his glass. We all clink glasses with each other and start passing dishes around our holiday table.

As I heap some food on my plate and dig into our Thanksgiving meal, I think about how I really am grateful to be able to help Grandma. That could be me one day, and I really hope someone who cares about me is there to help.

While Grandma eats, Mom slowly hands her each utensil because she cannot distinguish between them. If you don't help her, she'll try to use a spoon to eat a salad and a knife to eat soup.

> It can become difficult for a person with dementia to use eating utensils.

"Grandma, didn't you like the mashed potatoes?" Bentley asks Grandma as we're all finishing our food. Grandma used to make the best mashed potatoes, and they used to be her favorite, but this year Bentley helped Aunt Rita make them.

Grandma looked at her plate with a confused expression, as if to say, *What are you talking about? I finished all my food.*

"You ate everything but your potatoes, Mom," Uncle Dave says to Grandma.

Whenever there's a mystery around here, my mind now immediately considers the colors of things. I get up from the table and grab one of Grandma's special red plates from the kitchen. I spoon her potatoes from our fancy white china to her red plastic plate, and then the expression on her face changes immediately. Mom hands grandma a spoon, and Grandma digs right into her mashed potatoes!

"Good thinkin', Joe," says Dad.

"What just happened?" asks my cousin Kate. I explain that white-on-white is hard for Grandma to see.

"Tell her the welcome mat story!" says Bentley excitedly, and so I do.

---

If there is one thing I have learned about what Grandma is going through, it's you have to accept wherever the journey might take you. Change is hard, especially on holidays, which in my family is a time of year when we usually do everything exactly the same way.

Grandma used to be in charge of the kitchen on holidays, but this year, everyone else just pitched in and did it all together. And when it came to setting the table, Mom wanted to keep the tradition of setting the table with her special white china. But when someone you love has dementia, you just have to do what they need. Who cares if everyone has a white plate, and Grandma has her red one? When you accept that things are different, everything just goes much more smoothly.

Sometimes it's easier said than done though. The whole thing is definitely sad. As life gets a little more complicated for Grandma, it gets a little more complicated for us, too; and the feeling that we are losing her – her voice, her stories, her mashed potatoes – it's not easy. It hurts every one of us.

But, all things considered, this is still a pretty great Thanksgiving, even though Grandma has a few challeges and Bentley's mashed potatoes weren't quite the same. Who really cares? All that matters is that we're all together.

Over dessert, we look at old family photos together. I notice how much Grandma is enjoying being with everyone all around her. She's calm and smiling as she looks around at each of us. She pats our hands occasionally or smoothes our hair. Life's not always easy, but in that moment, I can tell Grandma knows she's with the people she loves and that we love her, too. As Mom would say, that's what it's all about.

As it starts to get late, Mom reminds Grandma she can go lay down in her room if she's sleepy. Grandma nods in agreement and gets up. On her way upstairs, she walks over to me, squeezes my arm, and whispers, "Thanks."

## JOURNEY TAKEAWAYS:

✓ Traditions are important to people with dementia. Remember that people with dementia can still take part in those traditions. You may need to make modifications to help them, but with communication and compassion, anything is possible.

✓ In this chapter, Grandma Mae had an accident and needed help picking out dry clothes. In most cases, you will want a parent or adult caregiver to help the person with dementia. Joseph decided he was comfortable enough to help his grandma. If he had not felt comfortable, he could also have discreetly asked his mom or big sister to come help. Remember, it is always okay to ask for help.

✓ Joseph provided his grandma with help, dignity, and respect, and that means a lot. People with dementia still have feelings, and they can become embarrassed just as easily as we can — sometimes more. Whenever anyone needs help, try to put yourself in their shoes and think about how they must feel. But, always respect your own feelings, too. You never need to do any caregiving task if it makes you feel uncomfortable.

# CHAPTER
## 10

# Mom Loses It

*C*hristmas came and went. New Years came and went. It is February and the snow is piled high on the sidewalks. The days are cold, short, and gray, and we're all trapped in the house most of the time because it's too cold to go outside when we don't have to. A full house was easier in the warmer months when we spent more time outside, but now we're all starting to feel a little cooped up, just waiting for Spring to arrive.

Mom has been distant lately. She drives us to school, picks us up, and brings us to our activities. But each time we get in the car, she turns on her radio station and stares straight ahead, which makes it hard to have a conversation with her. I remember when we used to talk in the car and in general have so much more fun together. She used to laugh all the time, be the life of the family -- but she seems sadder now and tired.

Emily and I talked about it the other day. It was one of the few times we've ever talked seriously and not bickered at all. We're both getting really concerned about Mom. We've noticed she's stopped doing simple things that she used to love, like going to yoga class with Mary or even getting a haircut.

It also seems like Mom and Dad barely talk anymore. Everyone just seems to do what they need to do on autopilot without taking any time to have fun with each other. It's obvious that having Grandma and Grandpa living with us is getting harder and harder.

Over dinner one night, Dad finally speaks up. You can tell it's hard for him to say something he knows Mom won't want to hear. "You know," he says, turning to Mom, "I'm just so darn proud of all of us for stepping up to the plate and doing what we've had to do. But, now I think it's time to get some help."

We all hold our breath a little, waiting for Mom's reaction. We all know what he means. And instead of objecting, this time, Mom nods.

The next day, Mom finally looks into getting more help from the Alzheimer's Support Center. She learns they have a Day Program that Grandma can attend two days a week. They also have Personal Caregivers who can come over and help Grandma get ready for each day and a nurse who can come check on her once a week instead of taking her to the doctor's office.

I wish Mom had known about these things at the beginning of Grandma's journey, but I guess sometimes you have to learn the hard way. What's most important is she knows now, and she's willing to accept

some help. I think things are going to get
better.

_____

After a few months of the Day Program
and Professional Caregivers, Mom starts to
get back into the groove of life. It's Spring,
and she's bought a few indoor plants, which
isn't quite as impressive as her usual,
vigorous outdoor gardening, but it's
definitely a step in the right direction.

One evening, I overhear Mom on the
phone, probably with Mary. "I am not
putting my mother somewhere to die," she
says, crying. "I just will not do it. I cannot do
it." I'm listening from the stairs. I know I'm
not supposed to hear this. The conversation
isn't meant for me, but it's a small house,
and I can't help but stay and listen.

When she gets off the phone, Dad is
there to her calm down and convince her to
at least consider the idea of visiting a few
Assisted Living Communities. Dad has a
pretty great way of helping people think
things through sometimes.

Over the next few weeks, Mom and
Dad research every old folks home nearby.
They narrow it down to two good ones that
they make plans to go and visit. Though we

were all invited to visit, Emily and I did our own things and only Bentley went with them. Still, we heard all about the communities as my parents talked about their visits at dinner each night. Bentley would chime in to add the fun details, like how one place had ice cream, and the other has a therapy dog who lives in the community and spends time with all the residents.

These conversations were very different than I expected. As they talked about everything the communities offered, it was like they were buying a new home for themselves. They would trade anecdotes about what they'd noticed about all the features and amenities. It sounded almost like they wanted to move in. Finally, Mom's spark of hope is back.

## JOURNEY TAKEAWAYS:

✓ Every person and every family handles things differently. Some people like to be alone when they are stressed, and others might need to talk about how they are feeling when they are upset. Keep an open mind and try to stick together.

✓ In this chapter, Joseph's Mom finally accepted she needed help. As the primary caregiver, she had taken on a lot of responsibility, and nobody can handle everything alone. Remember that it is important to communicate your needs and know when to ask for help.

*In the next chapter, you will learn a little more about Assisted Living Facilities.*

# CHAPTER
## 11

# A New Home for Grandma

*T*oday marks one month for my Grandma and Grandpa at their new home by the sea. Though it wasn't what Mom wanted to do, she knew it was time. Caring for Grandma at home had become too much. She needed nurses, activities, constant care, a place without stairs — all things we just couldn't do at home.

On the drive there, I didn't know what to expect. But, when we arrive, it looks like a hotel. The outside is painted a soothing light gray color and there are flowers and trees planted everywhere. As we drive around to the parking lot, we see a lovely green lawn where small groups of old people are playing games together. Beyond the lawn is a tall white fence enclosing the grounds beyond which is the gorgeous blue ocean.

"Whoah, this is like a resort," Emily says as Dad turns to smile back at us from the driver's seat.

"Pretty nice, right?" Dad says. "Keep an eye out for a parking spot in the shade — first one to find it gets a dollar!" It is nice to see Dad's playfulness coming back, too.

"Over there!" Bentley yells and wiggles in her seat excitedly about the dollar.

Dad parks and we all get out. We walk up the long, white ramp to the front entrance and walk in. Each person we pass on our way to the front desk smiles and says, "Hello," cheerfully.

When we get inside, I see the inside is even nicer than the outside. The walls are painted a sunny yellow color, and there's art hung everywhere – mostly of nature, trees, and the ocean. All the furniture is really nice and there's soft music playing in the background.

We check in with the young woman at the front desk who offers us cherry-flavored lollipops. She has Mom sign in and lets us know Grandma and Grandpa are taking a Tai Chi class. Both of my parents look at one another in confusion. My mother says, "Are you sure my mom is there?"

The young woman says, "Yes, I just saw them go in a few minutes ago. It's one of their favorite programs."

Tai Chi is a gentle form of exercise that can improve strength, flexibility, and balance.

We walk down the hall and find my grandparents in Tai Chi, both slowly moving to flute-like music. I have not seen either of them so focused in a long time. I look over at Mom and see her eyes tearing up. Dad puts his arm around her and gives her a hug.

At this moment, I know Grandma is not at the end of her life. She is just at the beginning of a new way of living.

We all watch my grandparents proudly for a few more minutes, then sneak out quietly before we distract anyone. We sit on the comfortable patio until the class is over, and then we meet Grandma and Grandpa in their room. Grandpa is so happy to see us and says, "Give us a hug." We each take our turn getting one of his big smothering hugs, and it feels pretty great.

I can tell Grandma is having trouble remembering our names, but clearly, she knows us. We each give her a hug and a kiss. After a few minutes, it clicks that Mom is her daughter. "Jeanie," she says, and everyone's mood relaxes.

Grandpa goes on and on about everything they have been doing, and Grandma chimes with a word or two here and there, too. Her speech is still a little jumbled, but it's better, and she just seems so happy. Finally, Mom asks them directly, "So, you like it here?"

Grandma responds, "What's not to like?" Mom's smile fills the room.

Grandma and Grandpa show us around their new space. It's like a little apartment. It has a bedroom and living room area, a bathroom, and a kitchen. The kitchen has a refrigerator but nothing dangerous like an oven, toaster, or cleaning products. Here, meals are served in a common dining room and they don't have to clean or cook for themselves.

This place has changed my mind about what an "old person's home" is. Seeing Grandma and Grandpa in a home of their own again reassures me there is so much life left for them.

Over the next few months, we visit Grandma and Grandpa regularly for parties, concerts, and other events at the community. Honestly, there's more on the schedule here than all of Emily, Bentley, and my extracurricular activities combined!

But, nothing is perfect, and as the weeks go by, Grandma starts to have more trouble keeping up. One day, the phone rings. Mom answers and I see the look on her face change from happy to scared. The community is on the phone, and they're asking Mom to come in for a meeting about Grandma.

That night I hear my parents talking in the kitchen. Mom is nervous they're going to ask Grandma to leave because she has been wandering more and more, and Grandpa cannot keep an eye on her all the time. That night, I think of my grandparents and make a wish that they will be okay.

All week, Mom's been worried about what will happen at the meeting, and today's the day. Mom picks us up from school and tells us we need to drive out to the community. "You can do your homework in the Sun Room," she says, which is fine with us because pretty much every room there is nicer than most people's houses.

Mom leaves us with Emily in charge while she goes into an office with a lady named Linda who runs the community. After about 20 minutes they walk out, and Mom has a smile on her face. She turns to us and says, "Well, Grandma does need to move, but only just down the hall."

Apparently, they have a section of the community for people like Grandma, where they can keep a closer eye on her to make sure she stays safe. The doors are locked so if she wanders, she can't go outside. This will keep Grandma safe, and also give Grandpa a break.

Linda takes us on a tour of the secure section of the community. They call it their Memory Care unit, and it's specifically for people who have dementia. It looks just as nice as the other parts of the community, and the residents are mostly sitting together as someone on the staff leads an activity. Everywhere we look there are activities going on. Linda tells us everyone who works in this section of the community is trained in how to work with people like Grandma. She will have even more people to care for her.

The first two weeks of the transition from one part of the community to the other was challenging, but after a few weeks, Grandma is doing amazingly well. Activities all day allow Grandma to be engaged while Grandpa can spend time with the new friends he has made. They play cards, and checkers. I think he even joined a book club! He joins Grandma for every meal and they sit together every evening. I think my wish for them to be okay has come true.

## JOURNEY TAKEAWAYS:

✓ Remember that so-called "old people's homes" may not be what you think. Joseph's family was fortunate to find a very nice place that could take good care of his grandparents.

✓ It is important for people with dementia to remain social with friends and family.

✓ It is good for older people to try new things. Exercise and new activities are good for the mind and the body.

✓ In this chapter, Joseph's grandparents have made some big moves – first to a new home, and then to separate sections of their new community. As we have learned, change can be difficult at first, but sometimes – if we can give ourselves time to adjust to a new reality – we will come to see the good side of our new situation.

# CHAPTER 12

# My Last Chapter: Not Grandma's

*T*hough this has been a difficult journey, our family has stuck together and gotten through it. Now, Mom and Dad have more time for each other, and my sisters and I are back to concentrating on our own lives. We're all feeling a lot less on edge. Mom's gone back to her job at the bank. And in case you're wondering what happened to Tina Brown, we are now officially a couple.

I learned so much from the experience of helping Grandma. I think back to how much it scared me to see her suitcases in my room. We went through so much together. Now, even though things are easier at home, I actually miss Grandma and Grandpa being around all the time. But I know they're receiving good care and doing so much more with their days. They have started a new chapter of their lives together. Each time we visit they are busy and smiling. You really cannot ask for too much more.

If I had to give advice to any of my friends who might have a grandparent diagnosed with dementia, I would first say to take a deep breath and let it out, slowly. This journey is going to seem like a lot, and sometimes things will feel scary and sad. Just remember: there is always a light at the end of the tunnel, and there is always something we can do to make things better for each other. Stick together as a family and treat others as you would want to be treated if you were in their shoes.

From time to time, one of our friends or relatives will say something insensitive about putting Grandma in "an old folks' home" but Mom just smiles and tells them what a benefit it has been and how lucky we are to be able to get them the care they need. "We are all changing," she says. "Some of us are just changing at a faster rate."

It is crazy to hear Mom talk so positively. Just a few months ago, she was so stressed out, these types of comments from other people would have made her cry. I am truly proud of my family for doing our best, knowing when to get help, and accepting the things that we can't change.

I think back to everything we've been through as a family. Some moments that were terrifying at the time are kind of funny now, and some things that were sad still are. One thing I know for sure now is I want to become a doctor when I grow up so I can help discover a cure for Alzheimer's disease. And on that note, I'm off to do my homework! Thank you for joining my grandma's journey by reading this book. I hope it has made you laugh, touched your heart, and given you courage to keep going even when life changes in unpredictable way.

# JOURNEY TAKEAWAYS:

✓ When you love someone with dementia, try to join their journey by thinking about how they must feel and trying your best to help them.

✓ Know that dementia is not the end of life; it's just a different way of living.

✓ People with dementia can still learn, love, and enjoy life.

✓ You are not alone, and no one can do everything without help. Ask for help when you need it.

✓ Nothing in life is more important than family. Family can be your immediate family, such as your mom, dad, and siblings; your extended family, such as your grandparents, aunts, uncles, and cousins; and it can even be your closest friends who you love as if they were family. Enjoy your time together and take care of each other.

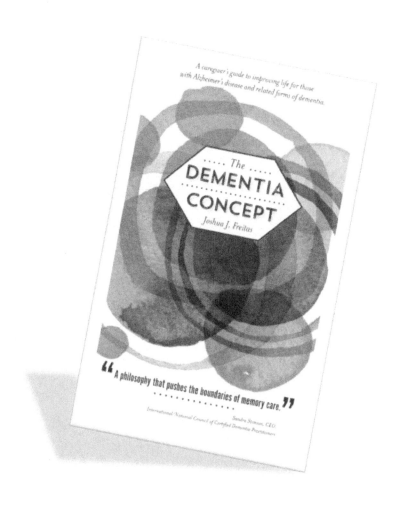

A caregiver's guide to improving life for those with Alzheimer's disease and related forms of dementia.

The
DEMENTIA
CONCEPT
Joshua J. Freitas

" A philosophy that pushes the boundaries of memory care. "

Sandra Stimson, CEO
International/National Council of Certified Dementia Practitioners

To learn more about dementia, check out an additional work by this author,

*The Dementia Concept* by Joshua Freitas.

42631854R00076

Made in the USA
Middletown, DE
21 April 2019